P9-DMB-472

THE SLING AND THE SWALLOW

BY ELEANOR HULL

Illustrated by
Arthur Polonsky

UNITED CHURCH PRESS
BOSTON, PHILADELPHIA

The following biblical passages serve as a basis for parts
of this story:
Chapter 1—1 Samuel 17:49; John 2:13–16; Matthew 21:13
Chapter 2—Amos 5:21; Exodus 3:18; 1 Samuel 17:49
Chapter 3—Matthew 3:1–12; John 1:21
Chapter 4—Matthew 9:1–7; 1 Samuel 18:1–4; 19:1–7
Chapter 5—Matthew 3:7; 4:12; 5:43, 44; Deuteronomy 6:5
Chapter 6—Mark 3:1–6
Chapter 7—Matthew 14:10
Chapter 8—John 3:1–21

Copyright © 1963 by the United Church Press. Printed in the United States
of America.

All rights to this book are reserved. No part of the text or illustrations may be
reproduced in any form without written permission of the publishers, except brief
quotations used in connection with reviews in magazines or newspapers.

Library of Congress Catalog Card Number 63-11064

This book is part of the United Church Curriculum, prepared and published by
the Division of Christian Education and the Division of Publication of the United
Church Board for Homeland Ministries.

CHAPTER 1

The Secret Thing

For once nine-year-old Seth thought it was a good thing to be small. He could work his way easily through the crowd. It was early morning. The sun had not yet come up, but all kinds of people were already hurrying about Jerusalem.

Seth ran under the neck of a camel. He hurried around the baskets of vegetables which stuck out from the sides of a donkey. He squeezed against the wall to keep out of the way of an excited calf that was being taken to the temple to be sacrificed. Seth paid no attention to any of these.

He was searching for two things. One was pigeons. His mother had given him and his sister Debbie each enough money for one pigeon. He was to buy Debbie's too. The other thing he wanted was a secret.

He saw the pigeons first. There was no danger of missing the bird-seller. He came walking along with the birds hung in nets over his shoulders.

"Doves!" he called. "Ducks! Pigeons! Beauties from the far rocks and high mountains!"

Once they had flown through the air. Now they looked like dead bundles of feathers. It was not until Seth came close that he saw their trembling wings and bright, scared eyes.

"Two pigeons, please," said Seth. The bird-seller did not hear him. Seth stood there and repeated firmly, "Two pigeons, please."

Then the bird-seller heard him but pretended not to see him because Seth was so short.

"I hear somebody, but I can't see anybody," he joked. "Where are you? Hold up your hand."

Seth did not like to be teased about being short, but he did not let himself get angry. This was just a silly peddler who lived in the wilderness.

"Two pigeons, please. I want them well marked."

"Oh, indeed, sir. Very well, sir."

The bird-seller pushed his brown hand into the net and brought out a bird by its feet. It was pure white with bright red eyes.

"Will this do for your lowness—I mean your highness?" asked the bird seller.

"Yes. That and another one."

"Yes sir, kind sir."

Seth thought, "I shall act like a grownup and pretend not to notice that he is teasing me. When I grow up I will be a lawyer of the Pharisees, like my father. A man like this will not dare to make fun of me then."

The peddler showed him another pigeon, a more ordinary one. It had black and white wings, a soft gray body, and a shiny purple neck. He would give this one to Debbie. She would love any kind of bird.

Seth paid the peddler and took the birds. Then something happened that made him forget about the birds and the other thing he wanted.

It happened every day at sunrise, yet it always made Seth tremble with excitement. At home he would run up to the housetop so he could see the temple. Here, in the market place, he had only to turn his head.

Seth heard three clear, sharp blasts from the silver trumpets of the priests. Just as the third blast sounded, the sun sprang into the sky. It made the great gold and white marble temple on the mountaintop shine with light. To Seth it seemed as though the sound of the trumpets was the sound of all the Jewish people thanking God for his goodness. And the rising sun was like God's answering smile. How wonderful it was to be a Jew, to be one of God's special people!

Then Seth heard the loud Roman bugles from the Fort of Antonia. The Roman bugles reminded Seth that the Jews were not free. Judea was ruled by Rome. Roman soldiers were everywhere. So far the Romans had allowed the Jews to worship God, but what if the Romans changed their minds and made the Jews worship the Roman gods?

If only David, the great king who had beaten the

giant Goliath with nothing but a sling, could come back
and rescue Judea! Or someone like David but greater
yet—the Messiah!

Thinking about David made Seth remember the
other thing he wanted. With a pigeon hung over each
shoulder, Seth pushed out through the gate and looked
down the path that led from the Mount of Olives.

People coming to Jerusalem for the Passover holi-
day walked along in small groups. Some of them sang
hymns as they walked. And there was a shepherd, leading a small flock of sheep.

"Benjamin!" called Seth, running down the hill.

The shepherd only glanced at Seth and walked
slowly and steadily uphill, speaking softly to his sheep.
Benjamin was very unhappy when he had to bring his
best animals to be sacrificed.

Seth walked along beside him. "You have brought
a lot of sheep," he said. "Is that a tenth of the flock?"

"Yes. A tenth and more too," grumbled Benjamin.
"Your father wants to ruin his flock."

"More too—why is that?"

"Giving 'em away, that's why. Don't you dare tell him I told you. Your father warned me to keep silent. But he ordered me to bring a dozen extra to give to the poor. He said that the Sadducees are keeping the price up in the temple market. So, as usual, your father thinks he has to help out those lazy good-for-nothings who want to make a sacrifice but can't afford to buy the animals."

"It is only right for those who can to give to the poor at Passover. They shouldn't brag about it, either," said Seth. "Instead of scolding my father, why don't you get mad at the money-changers who try to steal from people by giving the wrong change or at the Sadducees and their high prices?"

Benjamin did not bother to answer.

"Well, did you bring it?" asked Seth. He had hoped that Benjamin would give him the secret thing without his asking.

But they had come to the temple gate, and Benjamin was too busy to answer Seth. All the crowds were meeting and trying to get in at once. Benjamin's flock became bewildered. Some of them tried to go on past the gate and got lost among other flocks.

Benjamin gave a little whistling call. His sheep all heard it in spite of the noise and began to sort themselves out and come to him. Other shepherds were calling too. Each sheep knew its own shepherd's voice. Finally Benjamin got his flock through the temple gate.

"*Benjamin!*" pleaded Seth. He wanted to go home. He wanted to show the pigeons to Debbie.

Benjamin reached inside his belt for something and handed it to Seth. "Now don't get in trouble with it," he warned.

"Oh, thank you, Benjamin, it's fine! You make the best ones in Judea!" Seth cried, turning it over and over.

"I suppose half the strangers from Galilee will be staying at your house tonight. I hope your father will save a corner for his old servant," grumbled Benjamin.

"Oh, he will!" Seth laughed and ran off. Now he had everything he wanted.

A big bridge divided the temple from the part of the city where Seth lived. Seth started across it just as a troop of Roman soldiers reached the other end.

They took the full width of the bridge as they marched straight ahead, with clang of armor and stamp of feet. Seth and several other people had to get out of their way by rushing back to the other end. Extra soldiers were always brought to Jerusalem at feast time to "quiet" the people. Seth wondered if they quieted other people as little as they did him. They made him want to fight! He watched them pass, then crossed the bridge and went on up the narrow street to his own big house.

A servant opened the small door in the great gate when Seth knocked. He paid no attention to her, but was careful to touch the mezuzah that was fastened beside the entrance. Then he kissed his fingers. That was to show love and respect for the law of God that was held in the mezuzah.

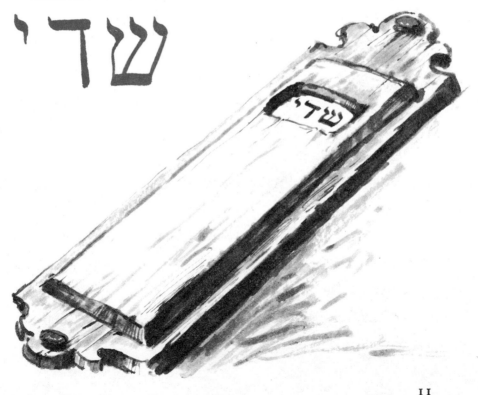

The yard was so full of servants that it was like a busy little town. They were getting ready for the Passover feast. Seth's mother herself was making the unleavened bread with Debbie trying to help.

As soon as she saw the pigeons, Debbie started jumping on one foot in her excitement. Seth thought that was pretty silly, even if she was only eight. She was a big girl, even bigger than her older brother.

"Which is mine? Is it that one?" she cried, pointing to the white pigeon.

Seth had to do some quick thinking.

"Yes, you can have that one—if you don't mind," said Seth. "Of course, the other is bigger. It will probably live longer and fly faster."

Debbie stopped jumping and examined the pigeons. She lifted each one. "The gray one *is* bigger, isn't it? Well, all right, you can have it. I don't mind."

She took the beautiful white pigeon he had picked for himself. Seth saw his mother's laughing eyes. He couldn't help laughing too. His trick had caught him instead of Debbie! He should have remembered that Debbie was often generous at the wrong time.

Well, anyway, he was older, and a boy. Boys were much more important than girls. For instance, he would have the main part at the Passover feast tonight.

That night, there were many guests around the long table. Some of the travelers who sat at the table were poor. Everyone was welcome at the Passover feast.

Seth's father began the special prayers and stories that were a part of the Passover meal. In his deep voice he said, "Blessed art thou, O Lord our God, King of the universe, who bringeth forth bread from the earth."

Then it was Seth's turn. He asked, "What is the meaning of all this?"

Then as he did every year, Father told the story of Moses leading the Hebrews out of Egypt where they had been slaves.

Everyone ate the good food and drank the wine. One cupful was left in the middle of the table for the prophet Elijah. Elijah was a great man who had lived long ago. The Jews believed he would come back some day to tell of the coming of the Messiah. The Messiah would be a greater king than David. The Messiah would be sent by God to save Judea from her enemies.

After the feast was over, and the guests had gone to their sleeping-places, the family was surprised to hear a noise in the yard. Who would be coming at this time of night? Home or synagogue were the only places Jewish people should be on the night of Passover. Of course, there were the Romans. Seth felt a shiver up his spine. Roman soldiers could march into anybody's house at any time.

But the servant came up the steps and announced, "Master Nicodemus."

Seth's father jumped up to greet his friend. Nicodemus was a very important man.

He must have been hurrying. He had to stop a minute to catch his breath before he said, "I have come to warn you about a possible revolt. The people are restless. That fellow from Galilee, Jesus, made a scene in the temple today. He upset the tables of the money-changers. He drove them out of the temple with a whip! He said the temple was supposed to be a house of prayer, but they had made it a den of robbers."

"And so they have," said Seth's father.

"Too true, and the people know it. They are ready to get angry about anything. There are crowds of people everywhere. If they try to revolt against Rome there will be much killing. We Pharisees must be ready to quiet the people down before they get out of hand. Now I must go on and warn some others."

He swung around to go, then paused a moment. "We must quiet the people if we can, but if necessary we must be ready to escape from the angry Romans."

The family sat still. Each had his own thoughts. Seth thought, "Escape? Never!"

He secretly touched the thing he had got from Benjamin, the thing Benjamin had made so strong and true. It was a small woven net with two leather straps. You put a stone in the net, held the straps, whirled it over your head till it was going very fast, then let go one strap. The stone flew to its mark with great force. It was a deadly weapon, a sling—exactly like the one David had used so long ago to kill the giant Goliath.

CHAPTER 2

A Surprise Trip

That night Seth had bad dreams. He dreamed he was trying to use his sling, but his finger would not let go the thong. The stone whirled uselessly over his head while enemies rushed down upon him.

When morning came, everything seemed as usual. The next six days of Passover went by, and nothing happened. Seth and Debbie began to train their pigeons. Debbie named her pigeon Snow, and Seth called his Bright Wings.

After Passover week, Seth went back to school. His school was in a synagogue. The students sat on the floor around the teacher, Rabbi Caleb.

First Rabbi Caleb helped the younger ones, who were still studying their first scroll, Leviticus. Seth was sorry for them, though of course Leviticus was the law.

You had to know the law if you wanted people to respect you and God to approve of you.

Some of the 6 1 3 laws were easy to understand, like the ones about not stealing, or killing, or lying. But the laws about what you could and couldn't eat were hard to remember. There were so many laws about how to make sacrifices that Seth didn't see how anyone could keep them straight.

Seth was now in the group that was studying the prophets. He asked Rabbi Caleb a question. "How is it that God told Moses we must sacrifice, but told Amos, 'I hate, I despise your feasts,' and said to take away the offerings?"

Rabbi Caleb smiled. He liked questions. "Many people were being unkind and unfair to others. Sacrifices without justice do not please God."

After school, Seth and his friend Reuben went outside the city gates to try out the sling.

"Say, you're good!" cried Reuben with surprise. "That stone went a long way." (He was one of those tall boys who thought that if you weren't big you couldn't do anything.)

"It's not hard to make it go far, but I want to learn how to hit the mark," said Seth. "Look how David hit

Goliath right in the middle of the forehead."

"I don't see how he could," said Reuben. "I have to look in three directions to see where my stone is going."

They practiced a lot. In time, even Reuben got pretty good.

Seth had forgotten about the excitement during Passover, and the strange Galilean who made trouble in the temple. Then one morning he heard the servants singing about it.

The servants always sang as they worked. They used familiar tunes, but made up their own words. Once in a while the servants sang really exciting news.

Seth was still half asleep when he heard something that made him sit up in bed.

"Our master is going on a journey,

Into the rough, wild north country;

And he is planning to stay some time,

So he will take his whole household. Alas!"

Then another voice took it up:

"Our master is learned, knowing well the law.

Our master is sent to question the meaning

Of the Galilean who threw out the money-
changers.

Our master is learned, knowing well the law."

Seth's father had been chosen by the leading Pharisees to find out why Jesus, the Galilean, was attracting such crowds. He was to discover whether Jesus was obeying the Jewish laws.

Seth jumped out of bed. He had never been to Galilee. What an adventure!

Seth and Debbie talked about their pigeons. Debbie said, "Let's leave them with old Miriam. She will take care of them."

Seth said, "That's just like a girl, to be scared to take them along. If we left them behind, old Miriam would probably cook them for dinner. Then she would claim they got away. Let's take them."

So they got a large basket cage at the market, and prepared covered jars to keep water and seed safe during the journey.

Little by little all was made ready, and at last one morning they started. As they went out the city gate Debbie kicked her donkey hard to try to catch up with Seth. "How far shall we get tonight?" she asked.

"We will have to get as far as Jericho," said Seth. "You can't stop on the road. It is full of robbers!"

Debbie looked up and down their long caravan. "There are so many of us—they won't dare attack us."

Seth and Debbie had never been east of the Mount of Olives. They were surprised to find themselves going down, down, down from Jerusalem. The road twisted and turned, always downward, while the air grew hotter and hotter.

Sometimes the road ran along the top of a steep cliff. Always a hill or a wall of rock hid what lay ahead. Robbers could jump on travelers without warning, rob them, and disappear.

Seth closed his eyes against the blinding white road. Soon he was asleep. He was wakened by Debbie's voice. "Seth! Wake up! They have left us behind!"

Seth sat up with a start. He saw no one but Debbie. "They are over that hill," said Debbie, kicking wildly at her donkey.

"Oh, we'll catch up," Seth said. He leaned back to slap the old donkey to make him go faster.

"But look! Look!" Debbie shrilled.

Seth turned around. Behind them was a hill covered with white rock. He saw a turban rise above the top rock.

Robbers! Seth reached for his belt and pulled out the sling. He fitted a stone and whirled it over his head. He let fly the stone straight toward the turban.

Crack! It hit the top of the rock. The head with the

turban rose into full view. Then a dozen black goats ran out from behind the rocks in every direction.

The goat herder shouted furiously at Seth. In between he said soft words to his animals. "Curses on the heads of bad stone-throwing children! Come, babies, there, there now, my dears. And blast out the insides of terrible brats!"

And now Seth's father came riding back in a hurry to see what the shouting was about. All of a sudden Seth realized he might have killed the goat herder. Seth wondered how his father would punish him.

On the whole, Seth thought he was lucky when his father only took his sling away.

CHAPTER 3

A Boat and a New Friend

Next day they crossed the Jordan river, and traveled north on the Roman road. As they rode along, they saw some men standing in the water. Seth's father spoke to a Pharisee near the edge of the crowd.

"What is happening?" Father asked.

"We are having trouble with that man in the river, the one wearing an animal skin. His name is John. Some call him John the Baptist because he baptizes people right here in the river. He says that even those who follow the law ought to repent like common sinners. He thinks we should give away everything we have! The worst of it is, the people think he is the prophet Elijah come back. He says the Messiah is coming. Crowds come to be baptized by him in the Jordan."

"In times like these, times of trouble and war, people take any crazy man for a prophet," agreed Seth's father. "I am on my way to Galilee to find out what I can about another trouble maker, a man called Jesus."

When they had left the Pharisee, Seth asked, "Do you think the Messiah will come soon, Father?"

Seth's father thought carefully before he spoke.

"We have been told that the Messiah will gather God's special people together in Jerusalem and rule them forever. When that will be, no one can tell. But I, for one, can hardly believe he will come as a strange man wearing animal skins, or as a Galilean preacher! The Messiah will have to free us from the power of Rome. It will take more than a sling to do this."

Next day they traveled on. They passed more fine towns, and stayed all night in busy cities. At the north end of the Sea of Galilee they hit the main trade route, and saw interesting sights all day long. But it was sad to see the many sick people who were on their way to the healing springs beyond Capernaum.

"There is a rabbi in Jerusalem," said Seth's father, "who can cure people. But he hides his power. If he didn't, he would never have time to teach. Sick people would bother him all day."

When they finally reached Capernaum, they were so tired that they hardly noticed the city on its lovely hills. They found the house Seth's father had rented and unloaded the animals. Seth found a place to hang the pigeon cage. Then he threw himself down to sleep.

The quietness woke Seth. This morning there was no stirring, packing, and loading for another day's journey, and no trumpet-call to greet the sun.

Seth lifted the curtain that hung over the open side of his bedroom. A whole new world was waiting for him to explore! If only Debbie were a boy to explore it with him. Seth stopped long enough to pick up some fruit and bread to eat. Then he quietly opened the gate and stepped out into the strange street.

A train of donkeys was passing. The little animals carried baskets loaded with vegetables for market. Seth decided to follow them.

In a few minutes he was on the wharf. Fishermen were busy with their nets and sails, shouting to each other as they worked. Smells of tar and fish filled the air.

In one boat there was a boy with a mop of sun-faded hair. He was handy; he did not make an extra move as he unrolled the sail. The boat rocked as he worked, but his bare feet never slipped. His balance was perfect.

"That's a boy who knows how to get about in a boat," said someone behind Seth. Seth turned around, surprised. He had not heard anyone coming. "But I think his feet would slip on a marble floor," said a smiling fat man in a white robe trimmed with gold. "Now you are different. You are the son of a rich man, aren't you?"

"My father is a lawyer," said Seth proudly.

"Ah! A lawyer! From the way you talk, I know you are from Jerusalem," said the man. "What are you doing so far away from home?"

Seth was about to tell him when he heard a shout. The boy in the boat was calling to him. "Hi there! You'd better hurry if you want that boat ride I promised you!" Seth was so surprised he didn't know what to do. What boat ride?

"Don't keep your friend waiting!" said the fat man. "I will talk to you another time." He turned and waddled up the street in his gold-strapped sandals. The fisher-boy stood and watched.

Seth went down to the boat. "I didn't ask for a ride!" he said. "I just got here late last night."

"That's what I thought." The boy nodded, as if to himself. "Well, how would you like to come along anyway? My father is too busy to come this morning. You could help me with the nets."

Seth had never been out in a boat. The lake looked exciting. This fisher-boy would be someone to talk to. Besides, Seth was curious. He tried not to remember that his father would not approve.

The boy jumped out to steady the boat while Seth got into it. In spite of this, it rocked back and forth. Seth staggered to the seat and held on with both hands while the boy shoved the boat off the bank and leaped into it. They were afloat! How smoothly the boat moved in the breeze and lifted on the waves! This was a better way to travel than bumping along on a donkey.

"You watch this tiller. Hold it steady till I tell you different. Then turn it this way when I say 'Right,' and the other way for 'Left.' I have to get the net ready."

The tiller worked backwards. Seth tried to keep it steady, while the boy straightened out the net. Seth turned to watch the boy as he stood on tiptoe and threw. The net—a large, round, fine-meshed one with little weights around the edge—rose up, caught the air like a balloon, and dropped gently on the water.

"Right!" shouted the boy.

Seth turned the tiller, the boy toppled over, and Seth hit his chin hard on the edge of the boat.

"You stupid fool!" shouted the fisher-boy. He pulled in the net as fast as he could. Then he put his hands on his hips and frowned at Seth.

Seth could do nothing but stare back. He knew it was his fault. In his excitement he had turned the tiller the wrong way. Suddenly the fisher-boy shook his head. He shrugged his shoulders and laughed.

"Oh, forget it," he said. "Everybody gets mixed up steering at first. I hope the net didn't get torn, though.

If it is torn, I'll have to get mad at you all over again."

He began to straighten the net again. Seth watched anxiously. There were no holes.

Seth kept his hands on the tiller and didn't turn around again until the fisher-boy told him to help pull in the net. They brought in several good catches. "That's about enough. Let's land and have some lunch," said the boy. The box in the bottom of the boat was full of fish.

Seth realized that he was hungry.

They landed on a lonely shore covered with black stones. The boy laid three stones together to make a little fireplace. He collected driftwood and built a fire. As he worked, he whistled a tune between his teeth.

Then he picked out four of the fish. They were flat fish, about six inches long, with comb-like spines along the back. The boy slit them with his knife and laid them on a rock to roast. Both boys sat silently. The roasting fish gave out a wonderful smell. Then they ate the fish so fast that they burned their tongues.

Seth stretched and leaned back on his elbow. He looked over the blue lake, then back at the fisher-boy. "What's your name?"

"My name is Daniel. What's yours? And what is a rich boy from Jerusalem hanging around the wharf in Capernaum for?"

"Oh, we are visiting here," said Seth. He didn't quite like the question. It was true that his fine clothes looked out of place here, and his Judean way of talking sounded strange. "My father is Simeon the Pharisee. He was sent here on important business. He's finding out about a Galilean who made trouble up in Jerusalem at Passover. My name's Seth."

"Seth," repeated Daniel. "Son of Simeon, the Pharisee." He got up and began to kick apart the fire with his foot. "This Galilean your father is finding out about—is he named John?"

"John? No. It's someone named Jesus." Then Seth remembered, "Oh, John is that wild man who stands in the river and preaches."

"Wild man? I guess some people call him that," Daniel said. "But other people think he is the prophet Elijah, come back to get ready for the Messiah!"

Suddenly Seth remembered something he had forgotten in the excitement of boating and fishing.

"Why did you call me like that this morning—as if we had already planned to sail together?" he asked.

"I just wanted to get you away from that man—for your own good," said Daniel. "I was afraid you would tell him something you shouldn't and get in trouble. His name is Marius. He is a spy for. . .he's a spy."

Seth was more curious than ever. "A spy for whom?" he asked.

"Oh, I don't know," said Daniel. "But he is always hanging around the wharf asking questions. He asked Big Timothy questions one day. The next day Timothy disappeared. We have never seen him since."

"He said he would like to talk to me again some day," said Seth.

"You had better keep away from him," said Daniel. Then he jumped up. "Look at that ship!" A big ship went by them. At least twenty oars were pushing and pulling in perfect time on each side.

"See, no sails," said Daniel. "The wind has died down. We shall have to row back. We'd better get started. Can you row?"

"I guess so," said Seth, looking at the big oars.

They were as heavy as they looked, and even harder to handle. Daniel laughed when Seth bumped himself on the chin. This made Seth try harder than ever, and he finally got onto it. Before they got back to the wharf, the boys were rowing well together. Seth had begun to like the regular pull and push that drove the heavy boat through the water so swiftly.

When Seth stepped out on the bank, he found it was dry land now that felt queer. It seemed too solid, and too slanted. It almost threw him.

"Want to come again tomorrow?" asked Daniel as he tied up the boat. Then he laughed. "You will probably be too stiff."

Seth had been about to say, "I won't have time tomorrow." His arms were sore and his back ached. Besides, if his mother had noticed how long he had been gone, his father might keep him in tomorrow. But this changed his mind.

"Stiff? Why should I be stiff?" he answered. "See you tomorrow."

CHAPTER 4

A Dead Swallow
and a Stranger

Seth and his family were eating their sabbath supper. Sabbath meals were always good. Here in Capernaum the finest fish and fruits could be eaten fresh. But the family around the table was not as happy as usual.

"What's wrong, Simeon?" Seth's mother asked.

"It is hard to believe that the man really matters," Seth's father answered. Seth knew he did not like to be angry on the sabbath. "As soon as Jesus came back from his trip around the country, he went to stay at Peter's house. Well, Peter is a good man, though only a fisherman. But now Jesus has begun to make friends of the worst people—tax collectors and thieves of that sort!"

"How could anyone be a friend of tax collectors?" asked Seth's mother. "Everyone knows they deal with the Romans and rob and cheat their own people."

"Not only that, he has taken up with Simon the Zealot. He is one of the crowd that wants to start a revolt against Rome."

"I shouldn't think good people would have anything to do with Jesus," said Seth's mother.

"Well, nobody of importance does. It is the common people who run after him. You see, he heals the sick. They brought a man on a stretcher to him the other day. The man walked away."

"Why, how could he do that?" asked Debbie.

"Many rabbis could heal if they wished," explained Seth's father. "But they have better things to do. This man won't turn away a single sick person. It makes no difference to him how poor they are. How can he expect to get the respect of the important people?"

"Well, if he is not dangerous, why don't we go back home?" asked Seth's mother. "It isn't good for the children to have nothing to do. Seth is getting behind in his studies."

Seth did not look at his mother. Whenever she asked him where he had been he answered only, "Down by the docks." He couldn't possibly tell her he was spending all his time out on the lake with a fisher-boy. Yet, he told himself, "by the docks" was the truth—in a way. He wasn't breaking the law about telling a lie.

Debbie was making signs to him. He pretended not to see her. Finally he reached under the table and pinched her. To cover up her squeak Seth cried, "There are the stars!" The three evening stars had come out. The sabbath was ended.

His mother bowed her head for the sabbath farewell prayer. "God of Abraham, Isaac, and Jacob . . ."

Seth and Debbie escaped to Debbie's room.

"Why did you pinch me?" Debbie asked.

"You were making faces. In one more minute Mother or Father would have asked what you meant."

"Well, I think they ought to know anyway," said Debbie. "It isn't right for you to be doing such a dangerous thing without asking them about it."

"Oh, I don't think it's really dangerous," Seth answered. He tried to sound thoughtful, but he could hardly keep from laughing. Debbie believed the wild story he had told her. "Think how surprised they will be when I bring home the treasure! All right, hand it over. You got it, didn't you?" he finished.

Debbie nodded her head as she handed him his sling.

"I found it in the bottom of Father's chest. I hope he doesn't notice that it's gone."

"We'll put it back tomorrow night," said Seth.

He and Daniel went fishing before the sun came up next morning. Only one other boat was out.

"Your father didn't mind your coming early?" Seth asked.

Daniel shrugged. "My father hardly notices what I'm doing these days."

It seemed strange to Seth that Daniel's father would turn over the job of earning a living to his twelve-year-old son. But Seth did not feel it would be right to ask questions. Besides, what did it matter?

"You've got your sling?" asked Daniel.

Seth showed it.

"I've got mine, too," said Daniel. "But I'm not very good with it."

That was what Seth was hoping. He was tired of taking orders from this uneducated boy. Daniel only laughed at Seth's learning. He seemed to think you could live well enough without even knowing the law.

They worked hard and soon brought in a good catch. They took the fish to the fish-seller. Then they were free.

40

It was a lovely day. Seth was glad at last to be climb-
ing one of the gentle hills of Galilee. They weren't rocky
and steep like the hills around Jerusalem. These hills
were green and round and covered with flowers.

"I told my little sister I was going to hunt treasure in some caves. I said I needed this sling for protection against robbers," Seth told Daniel.

"I thought your wonderful law said, 'You shall not tell lies,' " said Daniel.

Why did he say that? Seth was trying to forget it. Besides, Daniel wasn't supposed to know the law.

"Well, if we get a rabbit, it will be treasure," he said. "And these days you always need protection. Anyone you meet may be a robber or a wild man or a spy for King Herod."

"Spies!" said Daniel. "I don't even like to think of them. Let's see how good you are. Rabbits are easy to hit. How about hitting one of those swallows?"

The swallows were flying through the air above the boys. They wheeled and swooped, showing their pointed dark wings and silvery breasts. What a mark!

Seth took a deep breath and fitted his stone. Could he do it? He swung the sling, watching the birds sharply.

A swallow flew straight toward him. Now! He let fly. The swallow fell.

"I can't believe it," Daniel said.

The boys climbed to the top of the hill. Suddenly a man stood up and looked at them. It was frightening, especially right after Seth had mentioned robbers, wild men, and spies. Both boys turned to run.

But after a few steps, Seth stopped. The man didn't look bad. Besides, Seth wanted proof of his skill. Daniel would probably never admit he had hit the swallow unless the proof was in his hand. While Daniel rushed down the hill, Seth and the man stood looking at each other.

The man was not a robber because he had no weapon. He didn't look like a spy. He was as different from fat Marius as anyone could be. His face was suntanned. He wore a common brown-and-white striped robe. But he had no shepherd's stick.

If he was a wild man, he was all right now. He smiled and said, "Your friend has run away."

Seth felt rather proud of not having run. "Yes, he's only a fisher-boy."

"A fisher-boy in a city like Capernaum has to learn to run," said the man. Seth wondered if he had been a fisher-boy himself. "Why weren't you frightened?"

"I was, a little, but I thought I had hit a swallow. I wanted to find my swallow," said Seth, beginning to look around on the ground.

The man held out the dead bird, "Is this it?"

"So I did hit it!" Seth cried happily. He started to take it, then drew back. The little bundle of feathers reminded him of Bright Wings and Snow when he first saw them in the peddler's net. Only they had been still alive. Their hearts had been beating hard with hope. This bird could never hope again.

Maybe, when Snow and Bright Wings were trained and flying high above Jerusalem, they might be shot down too.

"I didn't really think about killing it," Seth said.

"I know. A person doesn't realize until he's taken life away that he can never give it back."

"Daniel kills fish. But that is to make a living—that's different." Seth felt as if he had to explain a little more. "I wanted to show Daniel that there was something I could do. Daniel is so big. He is good with boats, and I'm not. I wanted to show Daniel I could hit the mark."

"Like David," said the man.

Seth was surprised. "How did you know?"

"I guess every Jewish boy wants to be like David. He was brave and generous."

"Did you want to be like him too?" Seth looked curiously at the man.

"Yes, I did. Do you know what I most wished I had that David had? A friend like Jonathan."

"I guess everybody does," said Seth, thinking how completely different Daniel was from Jonathan.

"It was funny in a way," said the man, "that Jonathan would be David's friend and be so faithful to him. After all, Jonathan was the prince, and David was only a shepherd boy."

Seth was surprised. "But David was—David!"

"That's it!" agreed the man.

He was looking down the hill. Without a word, he smiled, and pointed. Seth turned to look.

There was Daniel coming around a clump of bushes. He looked afraid, like somebody who was ready to turn and run again the minute anyone even looked as if he might chase him—but he was coming back.

"Here comes Jonathan," said the man.

Then he clapped Seth on the shoulder. "And you're going to be David," he said.

CHAPTER 5

Two Storms

Daniel and Seth were better friends after that day. Maybe it was because Daniel had seen that Seth could shoot well with the sling. Or it might have been because he had seen Seth stand still when he himself had run. Certainly Seth had felt different about Daniel after he came back.

"I crept around behind the bushes, and listened," Daniel explained. "I could tell he was not a spy. He didn't act like one."

"What if he had been a spy?"

"I would have told your father," said Daniel.

It certainly was a good thing he hadn't! But anyway, the adventure had proved that they were something more than just two people who happened to be in the same place at the same time.

But storms come over the Sea of Galilee when everything looks clear. And storms can come over friendship in the same unexpected way. Both happened to the boys in one day.

The friendship storm came first. It was a bright morning, and everything should have been very pleasant. Then as they started out, they saw a strange boat on the lake.

"That fellow doesn't know how to sail very well," said Seth.

Daniel looked at the boat, looked a long time. "I know who that is," he said.

"Who?"

"Oh, just an old land-crab," said Daniel, and would say nothing more. He kept watching the boat, which was going the same way they were. He was very quiet.

"What's the matter? Why are you so quiet?"

"The fish swallowed my tongue for bait."

"No, I mean it. What's wrong? I know something's wrong. Why are you worried about that boat? Is something wrong with your family?"

"My family? There's only my father and me—except for Uncle Elias in Jerusalem. My mother died soon after I was born. Her brothers were Zealots. They were killed by the Romans after the revolt at Sepphoris. That was before I was born. Mother never got over it."

Seth had heard of the two thousand people killed at Sepphoris fifteen years or more ago. It had seemed like a story—far away and long ago. He had never expected to know anyone who had a part in that terrible story. He often dreamed of revolting against the Romans, led perhaps by the Messiah. But he always dreamed of winning—not of being defeated or killed.

"But that was long ago," said Seth. "You're not worrying about that today, are you? Is it that boat?"

"It's falling behind. Perhaps I was wrong." Daniel looked at Seth hard. "Can you keep a secret?"

Seth wanted to say, "No." He was afraid of Daniel's secret. "I guess so," he answered.

"You have heard of John the Baptist?"

"Yes, of course."

"My father is his friend. John has been arrested by Herod and locked up in a terrible dungeon."

"But why—why would your father get mixed up with that wild man?" Seth cried.

"That wild man?" Daniel looked angry. "You've just heard his enemies call him that. He lives in the desert so he can be free to hear the voice of God and tell the people. He says that people must care for each other and depend on God. That is more important than spending all their time trying to save themselves with silly rules."

"You're speaking of the law!" cried Seth, nearly choking with anger.

"John's speaking of the law, too, the greatest law, the *Shema*," said Daniel. "That you must love the Lord your God with all your heart and all your soul and all your mind. And that's not all." Daniel eagerly bent nearer. "My father thinks John is Elijah, come back to tell the coming of the Messiah!"

Seth cried, "If John were Elijah, he wouldn't let himself be captured by Herod!"

"He is, though! My father believes him, and my father knows!"

"What does your father know?" sneered Seth. "He's just a know-nothing fisherman!"

Daniel doubled his fists. "Your father is one of what John calls 'that brood of snakes!' And that Jesus that your father is after—John thinks Jesus is the Messiah!"

"Oh, go on! You're a Galilean fool. You're crazy," said Seth. He didn't care if Daniel did beat him up.

Suddenly the boat began to rock. While they were shouting at each other a storm had started. Without warning the wind had whipped up an angry mass of clouds from behind the brown eastern hills. Then the wind had come sweeping down the deep valleys in these hills. In a minute the quiet lake had become a wild sea.

Seth jumped for the tiller, while Daniel began to take in the sail in a hurry. As soon as the sail was firm, Daniel took over the tiller. He told Seth to dip out the water that was beginning to fill the boat.

Seth held on with one hand and dipped as fast as he could with an old pan. Many people had drowned in storms on the Sea of Galilee. But strangely enough, Seth thought less about drowning than about John the Baptist. If Herod had put him in prison, then Herod must be afraid of him. Maybe John was important after all!

At any rate, there was something exciting about a lone preacher standing up against a king! And John taught the *Shema*. He couldn't be all bad.

Now Daniel was part of this exciting story. After all Seth's dreaming of adventure, he found Daniel living it! But could he believe that Jesus was the Messiah?

The storm broke in on his thoughts. The wind was getting wilder. It picked up the boat and threw it into the waves. The water crashed over them.

"We're going under!" shouted Seth.

"You jump," yelled Daniel, "and I'll turn the boat over. It'll float upside down."

"I can't swim!"

Daniel tied his long belt to his wrist and gave the end to Seth. "Hang on!"

Holding the belt tightly, Seth jumped. Down, down, in the wild water, up again, choking and gasping, down again. The belt slipped from his hand. He was lost.

Then a rough hand took his shoulder, and dragged him up into the air. There was the boat. He reached out

thankfully and took a firm hold on the side of the boat.

For a long time they thought of nothing but hanging on. As one arm grew tired, Seth grabbed with the other. He hardly knew what he was doing or how much time had passed. But suddenly a loud, cheerful voice shouted, "It's all over, everything's all right!"

Seth opened half-blind eyes and saw that the sea had lain down flat again. The clouds were rolling on past, letting the sun shine through.

Daniel was grinning over the top of the boat, his hair plastered down to his head. He looked like a turtle.

Just then they heard someone shouting, "Help! I'm drowning!"

Seth saw a dark head bob up. "Over there!"

Daniel pulled himself up on the boat so he could see better. He looked hard a moment, then dived.

Seth watched as the two seemed to struggle. Then he saw that Daniel had the man round the neck and was swimming back to the boat.

When he reached it, he pushed the man up on the rounded bottom of the boat. The man was too tired to move, but held on, close and tight as a wet leaf.

"Yell, Seth! Yell for help! He's too tired to last long. And it's too cold for us too. HELP! HELP!"

"There's a boat! HELP! Give us a tow!"

The fishermen saw them and rowed over fast. They dragged them into the boat. A few minutes later, the boys crawled out onto the wonderful dry warmth of the beach. It was only then that Seth took a good look at the man Daniel had saved. "Marius!"

The man got to his feet, shivering. He climbed slowly up the bank without a look or a word of thanks.

Seth was amazed. "Marius was the man who was after you!"

"Yes. I think he was hoping that I would lead him to my father."

"He's your enemy! Yet you saved his life. Why did you do that? Did you know all the time it was he?"

"Yes. But you can't just let a man drown. Besides, Father heard Jesus say 'Love your enemy, and do good to people who do bad to you.' And my father said, 'What a change it would make if a few people did that.'"

"Oh, I don't believe that!" said Seth. "It's only natural to be good to your friends and bad to your enemies. Why, if you're good to your enemies they will just take advantage of you. Look at Marius—he didn't even thank you. Now he has probably gone off to do you some harm."

"I'd better get home and tell my father he was following me," said Daniel. "It may mean they are going to arrest us. We may have to leave Capernaum."

"But where will you go?"

Daniel said, "I don't know. Across the Jordan probably, to the caves in the desert—the same ones David hid in, you know. Maybe we will go first to my Uncle Elias, in Jerusalem."

"But how will I know where you are?"

"I'll whistle a tune—the tune I always whistle. You come out, and I'll tell you. Now we'd better both get home! See you later."

In a few minutes Seth, still dripping wet, tiptoed in at his own back gate.

CHAPTER 6

Trouble in the Synagogue

Seth thought he was going to get away with it. But when he reached the top of the stairs, Debbie popped her head out.

"Were you out in the storm?" Then she noticed his clothes. "Why, you're soaked! What happened?"

Seth thought of saying, "None of your business." Or he could tell her another wild tale, like the one about treasure-hunting when he made her steal the sling. That reminded him of the day he killed the swallow. The man had said, " You're going to be like David."

So he explained, "I was out in a boat that turned over in the storm. The boy I was with rescued me."

Debbie was speechless at first. Then she said, "How exciting!"

"Exciting!" Seth was worried about Daniel. It didn't seem like a game now but more like a bad dream.

Next day was the sabbath. Of course there was no fishing or getting away from the regular duties. Seth was memorizing some scripture when he heard a sound that made him drop the scroll. It was Daniel's tune. Starting down the stairs, he met Debbie.

"There's a boy in the street whistling for you. I bet it's the one who saved you from drowning!" she cried. "Can I go down with you and see him?"

"Will you promise never to tell anybody anything about him?"

Her eyes got wider and she stopped a minute. Then she nodded and followed him closely down the stairs to the back gate. "This is my sister," Seth explained to Daniel. "She won't tell. Has anything happened?"

"Not exactly," Daniel said, "but something important is going on at the synagogue. Come on."

"All right," said Seth. "But you can't come with us, Debbie."

Debbie looked disappointed, then that stubborn look came over her face. "Then I'll yell," she said.

"Look, you know girls can't come out on the street. Someone might notice you and tell our parents."

"I'll wear some of your clothes," begged Debbie.

"Well, hurry," said Seth.

She was back very soon.

"Hey, you make a good boy!" said Daniel.

She didn't look like a boy at all to Seth. Her head-cloth was on all wrong. She was just a bother.

"Well, come on, let's go," he said.

Many people were hurrying toward the synagogue. Something special must be going on there.

Seth had never been in this beautiful synagogue. But when they went in, Seth forgot all about the way the building looked.

Everyone was crowded around the edge. In the center of the great room Seth saw his father with a group of richly dressed Pharisees. A poor, bent old man stood near them. But what held Seth's eyes was the man who stood alone facing the Pharisees.

He was an ordinary man in a brown and white robe, but he was not afraid like the old man, or proud like the Pharisees. He was standing motionless, as he had stood on the hilltop. It was his friend who had talked to him about David!

Seth heard his father's voice. It didn't sound angry, but almost as if he were begging.

"It isn't lawful on the sabbath!"

Seth's friend looked quietly at Simeon the Pharisee. Then he turned to the poor man. "Come here," he said.

Seth saw that the man was crippled. One arm was crooked, the hand hung lifeless.

Seth's friend turned back to the Pharisees. "Is it lawful on the sabbath to do good or to do harm? To save life or to kill?"

The question and the voice were sharp. It was different from the questioning of most rabbis. And the question seemed to be directed straight at Seth.

Seth found the answer though he couldn't speak in the synagogue. He waited eagerly for his father to say it for him.

But his father did not say a word. The silence was
so deep that Seth could hear his hilltop friend sigh
deeply. When it was clear no one was going to answer,

he said to the crippled man. "Stretch out your hand."

With painful attention, the crippled man stared at him. Slowly, slowly he raised the crooked arm. You could feel the terrible effort he made as his bent hand straightened. You could feel the stiff fingers ache as he stretched them out.

At last Seth realized who this man was. The rabbi

who wasted time helping the sick. The Galilean who had driven the money-changers out of the temple. Jesus, the man his father was after!

"Now what do you think?" whispered Daniel.

The common people had crowded around Jesus and the crippled man. The Pharisees, talking hard, walked toward the door near Debbie, Seth, and Daniel.

"We'd better get out of here," said Seth, "before our father sees us."

As soon as they were lost among the crowd in a back street, Debbie pulled at Seth's arm. "Stop a minute! I'm all out of breath. Tell me what it was all about!"

"That was Jesus, the man Father came to question," said Seth.

"But—but he's not a bad man!"

"No. I know he isn't." Seth did not know anything else about it, but he was sure of that. Debbie felt the same way he did. He thought it might help to be able to talk it over with somebody. He looked at Daniel. Daniel nodded. So they told Debbie the whole story.

Seth and Debbie got to the sabbath supper on time and properly dressed, though a little out of breath.

They weren't surprised to find Father disturbed.

He tried for a while to seem smiling and pleasant, but as usual, his feelings boiled over.

"The man has gone too far this time!"

"Oh, dear!" said Mother. She watched Father closely. She was always ready to listen and to agree.

"He stood there in the synagogue, with six or more of us Pharisees facing him, and deliberately broke the law," said Father.

"Why, he was only helping the man!" said Debbie, "I thought you said we should always help others!" Mother and Father looked at her with surprise, Seth with an inner groan. There was an awful silence. Debbie realized what she had done. Her neck and face began to turn red.

"I went through the streets to the synagogue, but nobody knows," she said. "I wore Seth's clothes. Everyone thought I was a boy."

Pretty soon the whole story was out—that is, the part about the fall in the lake, the rescue, and the trip to the synagogue.

"You see," Mother said to Father. "I told you that we ought to take the children home. They never did anything like this in Jerusalem."

"That is no excuse," said Father. "Right is the same here as in Jerusalem. Seth, you must promise me never to go anywhere with this—this fisher-boy again!"

Seth could not look at his father. The way his father said "fisher-boy" seemed to change Daniel from a person to a thing. Seth would not promise.

"Very well," said his father, "then you may not leave the house at all until you do."

The evening stars came out that night with a cold glitter. They shone on no sabbath peace, only on anger and unhappiness.

The next day Father called Seth and Debbie to him. He gave them a long talk about the law.

"The law is greater than any one person. By keeping the rules given by God to Moses, you help all the people yet to come. And you keep the faith with Abraham, Isaac, and Joseph."

"But if Jesus hadn't done good to the crippled man, he would have done harm by leaving him as he was. Is it right to do harm on the sabbath?"

"Great is the sabbath," said Seth's father, "for it comes before all the other commandments of God."

Seth knew he was quoting from one of the wise men. Seth opened his mouth to argue, but suddenly closed it again. He glanced at Debbie. She looked quickly at Seth too.

Father thought he had made his point. He went on to quote other wise sayings about the sabbath. At last he finished his speech.

Seth and Debbie rushed for the back gate. They had heard Daniel's whistle while Father was talking.

They opened the gate and looked up and down the street. Then they looked sadly at each other. They were too late. Daniel was gone.

CHAPTER 7

An Enemy Becomes a Friend

Seth stayed in the house two days.

Then he promised his father that he would never again go away from the house with "that boy." By that time he would have promised nearly anything. He felt sorry for Debbie and other girls. He would hate to be kept in so much.

He made his promise carefully. He would not "leave the house" with Daniel. That was not to say he wouldn't follow or meet him. It was a tricky kind of promise, but it kept him on the right side of the law. Besides, he remembered what Jesus had said about David's being a shepherd-boy. The only thing his father had against Daniel was that he was a fisher-boy.

Anyway, he didn't spend much time thinking about that. He was much more concerned about having failed Daniel at the signal. And he was worried because Daniel had not come again.

The first morning he was free, Seth went to the
lake before the sun came up. Most of the fishermen were
still loading their boats. But Daniel's boat was neither
at the wharf nor on the lake. Seth was unable to enjoy
the smells and sounds and sights that used to be so thrill-
ing. Finally he spoke to a fisherman. "Where is Daniel
this morning?"

The fisherman only glanced at him. "How should
I know?" Then, as Seth turned away sadly, the man
went after him and took his arm. "It's best you don't ask
about him, see? Best for you, and him too."

Seth turned homeward. As he dragged his sandals over the stones, he thought, "This is the worst thing that has ever happened to me!"

It was not just losing Daniel's company. Seth was quite anxious about his friend. Had Daniel and his father been arrested by Herod's soldiers because they were friends of John the Baptist—and Jesus?

Debbie was worried too. In his room Seth told her about the fisherman's warning. But there was no way they could find out what happened. It seemed sure that Daniel and his father had either been arrested or escaped.

"If we could only *do* something!" Debbie said.

That's what Seth felt, too. "I wonder if we could pray."

She was surprised. He knew what she was thinking. Prayers were something you memorized for certain occasions, like the sabbath prayer: "Blessed art thou, O Lord our God, King of the universe. . . ."

"I mean, if he's King of the universe, he ought to be able to help. David always asked God for help. And Daniel said that the reason Jesus can heal sick people is because he prays to God for help," Seth said.

"But how would praying help Daniel?"

Seth thought, she can't quite understand—and I can't either. He said, "If you say, 'God, please help Daniel,' it might make you feel better. I don't *know* that it will help Daniel, but it might!"

After supper that night, the family sat on the roof. They should have been enjoying the coolness and the peace, but they were uneasy.

"John the Baptist has been killed by Herod," said Father suddenly.

The children looked at each other. How terrible!

"Oh, these killings!" cried Mother. "Oh, for the good old days when our country belonged to us, and all lived in peace together!"

"There have been few such times in our country's history, except in the time of David," said Father sadly. He walked up and down. "I can't believe John was a bad man. I think he was trying to preach the truth. But he didn't understand the importance of the law. And that is also the mistake of Jesus."

"Have they arrested Jesus?" Debbie cried.

"No. He has gone out of the town with his followers to escape arrest. I, for one, am glad. I think that we will go home," Father finished suddenly.

"Oh, good!" said Mother. "We will go back where we belong, and forget that all these unpleasant things ever happened!"

Seth and Debbie did not know whether to be glad or sorry they were leaving. They worried about Daniel. Did he need their help? Would they ever see him again?

The excitement of getting ready to move was welcome. It made them forget their worries. They looked forward to the journey. This time they were taking the shorter route through Samaria.

It was as much of an adventure to travel through Samaria as by way of Jericho. There weren't so many robbers, but there were the Samaritans. Samaritans were relatives of the Jews. They claimed to worship the same God. But the Jews looked down upon them, and the Samaritans hated the Jews. Both sides enjoyed doing unkind things to each other. It was like traveling through enemy country.

Their journey took them near a Samaritan town. When the caravan stopped at a well to get water, the pigeons got away. Debbie had taken them down from the camel-pack where they were carried, and was putting water in the little dish. She made the mistake of standing too near the camel.

The camel had suddenly sneezed, right in her ear. Debbie had jumped and dropped the cage. Bright Wings and Snow had flown through the open door and soared up into the sky.

Seth saw them rise. The sun shone on them. For a moment he felt joy. It was joy with an edge of sadness, something he had never felt until he killed that swallow.

But his joy in their high flying was immediately followed by fear. Would they ever come back? The caravan would not wait for them, that he knew.

Not only the caravan, but many women from the village were filling jars with water at the well. Some Samaritan boys had come with their mothers to help carry water, or perhaps just for fun.

Of course they saw the escape of the pigeons. Seth saw that they were pointing and laughing. They seemed to think the loss of his pigeons was the funniest thing that had ever happened.

But even while he was thinking that, one of the boys left the group and came over to Seth. "Are they your pigeons?" he asked. His way of talking was a little different from Seth's, but not so different as Daniel's had been.

Seth was too proud to speak to a Samaritan. He nodded.

"Will they fly back to you?"

Seth looked up at the pigeons. They were still flying happy circles in the sky. "I'm afraid not," he said.

The Samaritan boy nodded. "I'm afraid not, too. They are so glad to be free after being in the cage. They won't mean to leave you, but they may not come back in time. I lost a pigeon once—a beauty—that same way."

The pigeons had almost disappeared. "If only a hawk doesn't get them," Seth said. "They aren't used to hawks. Or someone might shoot them."

He looked over his shoulder at the well. The men were filling the storage jars—that meant all the animals had been watered. Soon he would have to leave.

Debbie, who had been standing still as a mouse, began to sob. "I said it was the camel's fault, but it was really mine," she cried. "Now I know they will get lost and die."

79

The Samaritan boy said gently, "Never mind, Little Sister, I have a plan. You can leave the cage with me. I'll wait and catch them. Then, if you will tell me where you live, I can send them to you by the next caravan."

"We could leave their food," agreed Seth eagerly. "They wouldn't be worried about a strange person catching them if the food and the cage were here." All three watched where the pigeons had disappeared. They watched till their eyes ached.

They heard the loading cries of the servants, and then they heard their father's voice. He sounded stern because they were standing with a Samaritan boy.

"Seth! Debbie! Mount at once! It's time to go."

Seth dropped his eyes from the useless search of the sky to the face of the Samaritan boy. It was a nice face, rather long and thin, blue-eyed. It was different from Daniel's, but it was the face of a boy who was a friend.

A very strange feeling came over Seth. He lifted both his hands and put them on the other boy's shoulders. "My name is Seth. My father is Simeon the Pharisee. Anyone will know my house in Jerusalem," he said.

"My name is Jacob," said the boy, smiling. "And I will send the pigeons if they come back."

"Then thank you with all my heart, Jacob, whether they come or not," said Seth. He would have liked to add something about his feeling that they were friends. He couldn't think how to say it, so he just gave Jacob's hand a hard grip and got on his donkey.

He and Jacob had been enemies. By doing a good deed for Seth, Jacob had made his Jewish enemy into a friend. So that was what Jesus had meant!

CHAPTER 8

Like David

Jerusalem looked very different to Seth when he returned. He had never known it was such a hard, rocky city. But after seeing the gentle green hills of Samaria and Galilee, Jerusalem looked like a lion ready to spring.

"I'm not so sure I'm glad to be back," he told Debbie.

"It's home," said Debbie.

"And we haven't got our pigeons," he said sadly. "But Jacob will send them. And we will have more fun together training them than we would have had before we left."

As soon as they were settled, of course, there were many things to do. It was good to be with his friend Reuben, and to be back at school. There was something going on every minute, so that he didn't have time to

wonder about Daniel all the time. The fears came often enough, however, and at those times he prayed, "O God, please help Daniel."

The pigeons did arrive. They were well-fed and carefully fastened into their cage. There was a note from Jacob too. So Debbie and Seth wrote a note back to him, to be carried by the next caravan. Father knew, but said nothing. After all, what could he say?

Things seemed quite as usual one day when Seth came out to meet Reuben to go to the temple.

The narrow streets were full of people as they always were at feast time. This was the time of Sukkoth, the Feast of Booths. Extra Roman soldiers were parading up and down the city as usual to "quiet" the people. Seth and Reuben were going to watch the ceremonies at the temple.

But just as he came out of his house, Seth was stopped—stopped by a perfect stranger. Seth was quite startled and a little scared when this man came over and

touched him on the shoulder. "You are Seth, son of Simeon the Pharisee?" he asked.

Icy cold fear came through Seth. Who was this stranger? Was he a spy?

"Don't be afraid," the man said. "My name is Elias. I have a nephew named Daniel whom you know."

Daniel had spoken of his uncle Elias in Jerusalem!

"Oh, where is he? Is he safe?" Seth cried eagerly.

"He is safe until now. I hope he is safe with you. I told him he shouldn't tell anyone where he was. But he said he had promised to let you know. We heard your father had brought his family back to Jerusalem. Daniel was sure you could be trusted."

"Isn't it dangerous here for Daniel and his father?"

"They are only stopping here on their way to the other side of the Dead Sea, where they will find a safe place. Daniel says to tell you he will go back to Capernaum when he can. He will meet you on the wharf some day!"

The man turned to go, but Seth seized his arm. "But can't I see him while he's here?" he begged.

The man hesitated. "Daniel said I was to tell you where you might find him tonight. Can I really trust you?"

"You can trust me," said Seth, his heart pounding.

"They are hiding in a little passage down in Solomon's quarries," said the man. He bent down, picked up a stick, and quickly drew a map in the dirt. "You had better copy that in your mind and then erase it from the dirt," said Elias.

He looked hard at Seth. "You'd better not come," he added. "It is a frightening, perhaps a dangerous, place at night. I didn't realize you were such a little fellow."

Seth watched him go. He bent down to study the map until he was sure he knew it by heart. Then he rubbed it out with his shoe.

"Hey, there!" Reuben called. "I thought you were meeting me on the bridge!"

Seth joined Reuben, as if nothing had happened. But the day passed like a dream. Seth knew what was happening. He did the right things, but underneath he was thinking, thinking, thinking.

Solomon's quarries! Those underground deserted caves were frightening enough by day. And how would he get out of the house? It was much harder here in Jerusalem, especially at Feast-time.

But on the other hand—"such a little fellow"! *Daniel* had thought he was big enough to come.

Each night during Sukkoth the family ate supper on the roof in the booth built of branches. This was to remind them of the shelters the Hebrews had lived in for forty years after they escaped from Egypt.

The booth was pleasant with its ceiling of leafy branches. Grapes and other fruit were tied to it. But Seth couldn't enjoy the special bread, shaped like a ladder, or the candles, or the prayers and verses always repeated at this time.

He was wondering, wondering whether he should go. If he should, how would he get away? Then something happened which seemed to give him answers to both questions.

One of the servants came to ask if she could spend the night in the booth of her own family just a few streets away. Before his mother could answer, Seth said, "I will go with you and carry the light."

It was not really needed at all, but Seth's mother looked at him approvingly. She thought that he was trying to observe the spirit of kindness of the Sukkoth.

"Come back soon," she called after him as he went out. He nodded. He hoped he would be back soon!

He left the servant at her home, and then with pounding heart, went over the bridge to Mount Moriah, where the white rock for Solomon's temple had been quarried. All boys knew the way into the old, abandoned quarries. They also knew that they must watch carefully to keep from falling down the pits and cliffs on every side.

Seth swung his light as he went down into the huge entrance cave. Swinging the light made him feel a little braver. Yet it also made the shadows fly across the ghostly walls and the dark pits that had been cut a thousand years ago by Solomon's workmen. He stopped swinging the light. He did not want to wake up the other dark patches. They were bats.

Where was the passage he was supposed to take? There, *that* must be it. He was starting toward it when he stopped short. He heard sounds and saw a dim light coming from that very passage.

At first he thought it might be Daniel and his father, but in a moment his heart sank. These—now he knew, and he turned and began to run—these were the loud, bold shouts of soldiers!

He blew out his light, and stumbled along as best he could. He was breathing hard. Sometimes he had to crawl on his hands and feet.

Suddenly two soldiers came around a turn in the passage—two soldiers and a boy and a man. Other soldiers followed. Seth did not wait to see how many. He felt fresh air on his face. At the same moment he saw a little light—and was out of the quarry. Now he could run. He ran as never before, up one street, down another.

Finally he realized that he hadn't heard the soldiers for a long time. They had probably turned north to the Fortress of Antonia. He found his way back to the bridge, and crossed it to the familiar part of the city where he lived.

A kind of weak thankfulness came over him when
he saw his own house. But his mind was still full of
terror. The boy and the man had been Daniel and his
father.

And now that the Roman soldiers had taken them —well, there was hardly any hope at all.

As he came to his own gate, Seth tried to think what hope there might be. He kept saying over and over in his mind, "O God, please help Daniel."

And suddenly he knew. The knowledge came to him loudly, as if a great bell was ringing close to his ears. God was answering the prayer he had so often prayed!

The Roman governor, Pilate, had final power. But his power came partly from the Jewish people and their ruling body, the Sanhedrin. The Sanhedrin might be able to save Daniel.

Seth's father was not a member of the Sanhedrin, but he was respected by them. And Nicodemus—their friend Nicodemus—was a member of the Sanhedrin.

If Seth told his father what he knew about Daniel and his father, he might ask for help from Nicodemus.

His father *had* said, "I don't think John the Baptist was a bad man."

But how many things Seth would have to admit! Would his father punish him? Would his father ever forgive him? Would Seth ever, after such strange doings, grow up to be a respected person in the city, a leader?

But Jesus had said to him, "David and Jonathan." And Jesus had said, as if he were sure of it, "You're going to be like David."

"Is that you, Seth?" called his mother as the servant unbarred the door to let him in. "You were gone a long time. I was anxious. What happened?"

"A lot happened, Mother," he answered. "May I speak with you and Father? I want Debbie here, too."

It was a strange, hard story to tell. Mother's face was terrified. Father's face was grim. But Debbie's was sympathetic to every word.

When he had told all that he remembered, there was a silence. It was an awful silence. Like the dark, it could be hiding anything—anger, refusal, punishment.

Then Father said, "While I was working in the marketplace and synagogue to keep pure the faith of Abraham, that very faith was changing in my own home.

"However, all that will have to be talked over between us later. I don't think your friend and his father have done anything for which they should be punished by the Romans. I think Nicodemus might feel the same. We will go to talk with him."

A few minutes later Seth was again walking through the dark streets, this time with his father and two servants carrying lights.

Nicodemus was surprised to see them. He frowned while Seth tried to tell his story again. He could hardly get through it this time, but his father helped him when he broke down. And his father told it fairly.

When he was through, Nicodemus walked once or twice up and down the room. Then he turned and looked at them. "I think the Sanhedrin can save your friends—they are not very important to Rome. But *will* the Sanhedrin save them?"

"If anyone can get them to, it is you, Nicodemus," said Seth's father.

"Perhaps that is so," admitted Nicodemus. "But should I?"

"I feel that they have done no wrong, Nicodemus —that is, no wrong deed. They just don't understand the law."

Nicodemus turned to face Seth's father. "I never told you, Simeon, but I once talked with Jesus. It was after he threw the money-changers out of the temple. He spoke a great deal of the Spirit. I didn't understand all that he said, but it has never left my mind. Sometimes I feel that he was right, and that by loving all people you do more for God than by just trying to follow his rules."

A feeling of wonder came over Seth. For a moment he forgot even Daniel. He couldn't yet understand. But perhaps, when he was older, he could learn what Jesus was teaching. Perhaps he could follow it without having to turn against the pure Jewish faith. Perhaps. Nicodemus looked down into his worried face and smiled. He laid a hand on Seth's shoulder.

"We shall do everything we can," he said. "And when Daniel and his father are free, I shall tell them that Daniel has a good friend."

Seth felt a warm glow all through him. He had been like David.

Word List

NAMES OF PLACES

Ca-per'na-um
E'gypt
Fort of An-to'ni-a
Gal'i-lee
Jer'i-cho
Je-ru'sa-lem
Jor'dan
Ju-de'a
Mount Mo-ri'ah
Rome
Sepph'o-ris (sef'o-ris)
Sol'o-mon's quarries

NAMES OF PEOPLE

Ben'ja-min
Cā'leb
Dan'iel
E-lī'as
E-lī'jah
Go-lī'ath
Jon'a-than
Mar'i-us
Mir'i-am
Nic'o-dĕ'mus
Reu'ben (roo'ben)
Sim'e-on

JEWISH RELIGION

Feast Days
Le-vit'i-cus
Mes-sī'ah
me-zu'zah
Passover
rab'bī
She-ma'
Suk'koth (sook'eth)
syn'a-gogue (sin'a-gog)

IMPORTANT GROUPS

Phar'i-sees (făr'i-sēs)
Ro'mans
Sad'du-cees
San'he-drin
Zeal'ots (zel'uts)

OTHER NEW WORDS

proph'ets (prof'ets)
sac'ri-ficed (sak'ri-fīsed)
un-leav'ened